HONK!
HONK!

For Charlotte

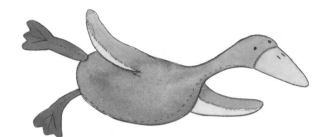

KINGFISHER
An imprint of Kingfisher Publications plc.
New Penderel House
283-288 High Holborn
London WC1V 7HZ

First Published by Kingfisher in hardback 1997
ISBN 0 7534 0114 2
1 3 5 7 9 10 8 6 4 2

First Published by Kingfisher in paperback 1998
ISBN 0 7534 0294 7
1 3 5 7 9 10 8 6 4 2

A CIP catalogue record for this book is available from the British Library.

Edited by Sue Nicholson
Designed by Rebecca Elgar

Typeset in Seagull
Printed in Hong Kong

HONK!
HONK!

Mick Manning and Brita Granström

KINGfISHER

honk!
honk!

A goose landed outside my window
last night, a wild goose, flying north.

I put my arms around her neck,
I climbed on her back, and she carried me away.

We flew above the city lights,

above railroads and highways,

above lakes and fields.

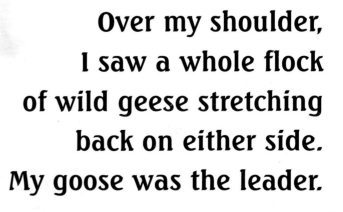

honk!
honk!

Over my shoulder,
I saw a whole flock
of wild geese stretching
back on either side.
My goose was the leader.

honk!
honk!

Others joined us.
We became a huge honking flock.
Hundreds of wild geese, all flying north.

North! In wind and rain.

North! By night and day.

North! In sunshine and moonlight.

When we rested,
sentries stood guard.
If one beady eye spotted
a creeping fox, then . . .

honk!
honk!

. . . we would take off with
a WHOOSH of goose wings.

honk!
honk!

We flew on, always north.

North! Dodging the hunters and hawks.

North!
Over snowy mountains
and icy rivers.
Always north.

We arrived at the nesting grounds.

honk!
honk!

honk!
honk!

My wild goose
met her friends,
laid her eggs . . .

. . . and hatched five fluffy goslings.

As the summer ripened, the goslings

grew bigger . . . and bigger . . .

and bigger.

ho...
hon...

h
h

honk!
honk!

They learned to fly.
They learned to speak.

As the short summer came to an end,
the ice began to creep back over the lake.
The sun sank low in the sky.
Winter was returning.

**honk!
honk!**

Wild goose stretched
her wings.
It was time to
return South again.

I climbed on wild goose's back
and we took to the air.
We circled higher and higher
calling all
her family
together.

honk!
honk!

honk!
honk!

honk!
honk!

Then we began our journey home.

South! Dodging the hunters and hawks, foxes and wolves.

South! Over electric cables and railway lines.

South! In wind and rain, by night and day.

honk!
honk!

South! To my window.

Goodbye and good luck wild goose!

WILD GEESE

GOOSE FACTS

Geese belong to the same bird family as ducks and swans. These birds are often called waterfowl because they live on or near water. Geese have large webbed feet to help them paddle, and oily feathers to keep them dry and warm.

Canada goose

Webbed feet →

← Oily feathers

KINDS OF GOOSE

Farmyard goose

There are over 40 different kinds of wild goose. The Canada Goose is the most common wild goose living in North America. It is also found in parts of Europe and Asia. The domesticated white goose seen on many farms is descended from the Greylag goose.

GOOSE CALLS

Most geese make a loud honking sound but some, like the White-fronted goose, cackle. Others even bark like small noisy dogs.

LIVING IN PAIRS

Geese usually live in pairs, especially when they are nesting and raising their young. However, geese often join together for safety or when travelling. A group of geese is called a gaggle.

GOOSE EGGS

Geese usually lay five to six eggs. Goose eggs are different colours. Some are creamy white, some are blue and some are greenish. Most are usually twice as big as a hen's egg.

Goose egg

Hen's egg

FLYING GEESE

On long journeys, most geese fly in lines, forming a big V-shape in the sky. Different geese take it in turns to be the leader at the point of the V.

Flying in a group in a V-shape makes it easier for the geese to push through the air so they don't get as tired and can fly more quickly and for longer. A V-shape of flying geese is called a skein.

GOOSE JOURNEYS

Most geese spend the summer in the far north, where they nest and rear their goslings, and fly south for the winter when the northern lands get too cold and harsh. This movement of birds and other animals at certain times of the year is called migration.

OTHER TRAVELLERS

Butterflies, eels, salmon and many kinds of bird migrate, too. Every year, North American Monarch butterflies migrate from Mexico and California as far north as Canada. The Arctic tern flies from the Arctic to the Antarctic – a distance of 12,000 km.

Arctic tern

Eel

Salmon

Monarch butterfly